A welcome from Martin Roberts

I'm delighted to be providing you with this special 'Teaching Version' of my children's book, Sadsville.

Working in support of and with the endorsement of the NSPCC and Childline, I created Sadsville to help children deal with emotions, especially sadness, and in a light hearted way, open up discussions about mental well being.

Through my charity, the Martin Roberts Foundation, we've already sent out tens of thousands of copies of the original Sadsville book to children in primary schools around the country, and the feedback from teachers and pupils has been overwhelmingly positive. Over 70% of the children surveyed felt 'better able to cope with sadness' as a result of reading the book.

Now, thanks to the kind donation from Wasdell Group we are able to supply all primary schools in the UK with a copy of this special Teaching Version of the book, which contains not only the original story, but a fully structured and detailed lesson or assembly plan, a self help guide for kids and a directory of relevant support organisations.

There are many more fantastic resources available free of charge at www.sadsville.co.uk - including a charming video version of the book read by Basil Brush and a visually stimulating powerpoint presentation to accompany the lesson plan. In addition you can find a free read-along version of Sadsville for tablets at www.fonetti.com.

Times are tough for young people, and the challenges they face seem greater than ever before. I hope you find this book useful and that it goes some way towards helping you steer your children on the right path, and encouraging them to reach out for support if they need it.

with all good wishes

TV Presenter & Children's Author
www.martinroberts.co.uk

Basil Brush reads 'Sadsville'
Ideal for children of all ages to enjoy at any time or to use in the classroom.
Go to: sadsville.co.uk

Self Help
A Self Help Guide for children is at the back of this book.
Also visit: sadsville.co.uk for more tips for childhood wellbeing for parents and carers, and a children's workbook.

Teaching Aids
To help you introduce Sadsville in your setting. Including presentation & worksheets.
All available for FREE from: sadsville.co.uk

A digital 'read along' version available on
fonetti.com

Video

Self Help

Resources

Read Along

HERMAN... AND THE MAGICAL BUS

TO

SADSVILLE

WRITTEN BY
MARTIN ROBERTS

ILLUSTRATED BY
JACKIE GEOGHEGAN

CHAPTER ONE

Tears streamed down the face of a glum
looking sun as it crawled above the horizon.

A hedgehog uncurled from its tight ball of prickles, wiped its eyes and decided to curl up again.

A sheep, not generally known for expressive emotion, took a large clump of grass in its mouth and chewed, gloomily.

A horse in the same field snorted, huffed, puffed and went for a gallop to try and cheer itself up.

And from behind the front door of a house a few fields away a muffled sniffing noise could be heard.

Inside, Sandi, the saddest person in Sadsville pulled another tissue from the box, wiped the tears from her eyes and blew her nose noisily.

"NOT ANOTHER DAY OF FEELING SAD,"

she said to herself loudly.

"I need to cheer myself up"

She turned on her smart phone and someone had sent her a text.

"I can't stop crying," it said, followed by a 'gloomy face' symbol :O(

Sandi stared blankly at her computer screen and saw a reflection of herself in the shiny metal. Her eyes were red, her nose was red, her mouth drooped at the edges.

"This is rubbish," she said.

"WHY IS EVERYONE ALWAYS SO SAD IN SADSVILLE?"

CHAPTER TWO

Meanwhile, in a small town not a million miles away from Sadsville, Herman the hero of our story was just pouring some cold milk on his breakfast cereal. He tested the temperature with his thermometer.

"Not too cold, not too hot." he congratulated himself.

Herman lived with his Great Aunt Edna in a small neat house. His brothers and sisters had already left home when Great Uncle Arthur died, so Herman offered to move in with Great Aunt Edna to keep her company.

He liked her home because it was full of old fashioned things. Old clocks. Old pictures. Old scientific equipment from the days when Great Aunt Edna was a science teacher. He liked them because he was rather old fashioned himself.

Even his name was old fashioned!

9

Mind you, Herman had always been slightly different to his friends. While other children his age were playing with their computers and video games, Herman preferred reading books and particularly looking at old maps.

Some of the other kids called him 'square' which he thought was uncalled for. Herman prefered 'eccentric', which he had looked up in his favourite leather bound dictionary.

eccentric – *noun.* Deviating or departing from conventional or normal forms of behaviour.

Herman decided he quite liked being *eccentric*, so when he found a cupboard full of Great Uncle Arthur's old clothes, he decided to wear them.

Knee length tweed trousers, tweed jacket with padded leather elbows and a smart tweed flat cap. With strong walking boots, a compass and an old pair of binoculars around his neck, he decided he looked like an old fashioned explorer.

ALL HE NEEDED NOW WAS AN ADVENTURE.

CHAPTER THREE

Back in Sadsville, everyone was getting on with their day.

The lady who ran the roadside snack bar, stocked the shelves with cakes, biscuits and of course, everyone in Sadsville's favourite; cheese and onion crisps.

She had to stop every few minutes to dry her eyes.

"Another gloomy day in Sadsville," she lamented.

She decided to cheer herself up with a packet of crisps. But these were no ordinary crisps. They were the finest hand cooked crisps that money could buy, made at Sadsville's very own gourmet crisp factory.

And everyone in Sadsville loved them.

11

CHAPTER FOUR

Herman was looking through some of the books on his Great Aunt's book shelves. He was particularly fond of the extensive collection of old train, bus and ferry timetables. Others might have considered them boring, but Herman could happily spend hours studying the long tables of times, routes and destinations.

He traced his finger along the bookshelf and stopped on a timetable he was sure he hadn't seen before.

"BUSES TO THE VILLES", it said in large letters along the spine.

"The Villes?" he questioned.

"Where are The Villes?"

Herman remembered from French class that the French word for a town or village was a *ville*, but France was a long way from Great Aunt Edna's house.

He opened the faded pages. There was a long list of places Herman had never heard of; Boredsville, Fullsville, Tiredsville, Slowsville, Latesville, Coldsville, Windyville... the list went on and on.

Herman picked one at random and turned to the corresponding timetable page.

But instead of the long list of times he expected, it said the strangest thing.

The bus will arrive 2 minutes after you reach the bus stop.

He turned to one of the other pages for a different Ville and it said the same thing.

The bus will arrive 2 minutes after you reach the bus stop.

"*How very odd*", thought Herman.

"*This must be a very special bus if it goes to all these different places and knows when I'm at the bus stop.*"

"*It sounds,*" he paused.

"*Like a* MAGICAL *bus. Just the sort that could take me on an adventure.*"

13

CHAPTER FIVE

Back in Sadsville, Sandi was heading to school.

She'd packed her own lunch of sandwiches, a cereal bar and of course a packet of cheese and onion crisps.

She locked the house and set off.

At the end of the road she noticed her friend Ella.

Ella looked sad.

"What's the matter?" said Sandi.

"Oh, just... things are making me sad and I don't know what to do about it," explained Ella.

"I know, me too," said Sandi and she gave Ella a hug.

They both felt a little better, knowing they weren't the only ones that were sad.

"WHY ARE WE ALWAYS SAD?" said Sandi.

"SURELY THIS ISN'T HOW IT'S MEANT TO BE?"

"No," said Ella.

"But I don't know what to do about it. Maybe there's someone who can help."

"I'm sure there is," they both said at exactly the same moment.

And they laughed for the first time that day.

CHAPTER SIX

Meanwhile in that village not a million miles away Herman closed the front door of Great Aunt Edna's house, checked he had everything he needed for a day of adventures and set off down the familiar road towards the local shops.

A short distance from his front door a Bus Stop had appeared.

"That's odd," thought Herman.

"I don't remember seeing that before. It certainly wasn't there when I went to bed last night."

"How strange."

Even stranger, was the timetable that was attached to the Bus Stop pole.

BUSES TO THE VILLES

...it said in big letters, and underneath it simply said,

The next bus will be along shortly

"The next bus to where?" said Herman out loud.

"And how does it know when I'm... is there... what if I... but how can?"

Before Herman could get any more confused, a big red double decker bus appeared over the crest of the hill.

This in itself was surprising, as the only time Herman had ever seen a red double decker bus before was when he went to London. So what was the bus doing here?

Then he noticed something even more odd.

This was a very old fashioned double decker bus, just like the one on the front cover of the old dusty timetable he'd found on Great Aunt Edna's bookshelves.

Old buses like this had a section on the front at the top which the driver could wind up and down to show different destinations.

As the bus drew closer Herman could read what it said. In black letters on a white background was written one word: 'Sadsville'.

"Oh dear that doesn't sound like a very happy place," Herman said to himself.

"But if that's where the bus is going then I guess that's where I'm going."

CHAPTER SEVEN

Sandi and Ella were sitting eating their lunch.

"I'm saving my crisps till last," said Ella.

"Me too," said Sandi then "Oh no..."

She stopped.

"I've forgotten my crisps. I'd better go to the shop and buy some. I can't have my meal without crisps!"

They looked up just as a big red double decker bus pulled up by the line of shops in the centre of Sadsville.

"I've never seen one of those here before," said Ella.

"Me neither," said Sandi.

"Thank you," said Herman to the bus driver who appeared to be crying.

"Mmmmmm... my... ppppp... pleasure," he sniffed as Herman got off.

"He doesn't seem very happy," thought Herman.

As Herman walked down the street, he noticed that everyone seemed sad. All the people walking towards him were drying their sad eyes with hankies.

Dogs with droopy jowls looked even more glum than usual!

Even the flashing animated characters on the pedestrian crossing seemed gloomy.

"Why on earth is everyone so sad?" thought Herman.

"SOMETHING VERY SAD MUST HAVE HAPPENED HERE."

CHAPTER EIGHT

While he was mulling this over Herman decided he needed a snack. He often found that he could think more clearly after a chocolate biscuit or a piece of Battenburg cake.

He noticed a cafe on the high street and arrived there at the same time as Sandi.

"After you," he said politely as Sandi and him nearly collided at the door.

"Thank you," Sandi said as they walked up to the counter.

"A packet of cheese and onion crisps please," she said to the lady who was serving.

"Crisps," thought Herman. "What a good idea."

On the counter was a big glass bowl full of packets of very special looking crisps.

'Brian's Hand Cooked Crisps'

announced the elaborate sign.

'Made locally... with the finest ingredients.'

"A packet of cheese and onion crisps for me too," said Herman when his turn came.

He paid the lady, then walked outside to where Sandi and Ella were sitting on a bench. He sat down on another nearby.

Herman couldn't help noticing that the two girls seemed to be crying.

"Are you OK?" he asked.

"We're just so sad," said Ella.

"And we don't know why," said Sandi.

"Oh dear," said Herman in a very concerned manner.

He tore open the crisp packet and was immediately overcome by the strong smell of cheese and onion coming from inside. He reached inside the packet but instead of pulling out a crisp he found a large chunk of cheese and a slice of very stinky onion!

The smell from the onion was so strong that it immediately made his eyes sting and he started to cry.

"Excuse me," Herman said to Sandi and Ella, "can I just see your packet of crisps?"

Sandi passed over her packet.

Sure enough there amongst the hand fried pieces of potato crisps were large chunks of cheese and slices of raw onion.

Herman had an idea.

"Do you know where these crisps are made?" he asked.

"In a factory on an industrial estate just up the road," said Sandi.

"Can you show me the way there?" said Herman.

"I have an idea why everyone in Sadsville is sad!"

CHAPTER NINE

"Where are you from?" asked Sandi as they walked up the street towards the factory.

"A town not a million miles away," explained Herman.

"Random," said Sandi.

"But cool jacket," Sandi continued, "Is it Burberry?"

"No, it's my Uncle Arthur's," said Herman.

"I've seen something like that on the London Fashion Week reviews on the internet," said Sandi.

"I don't use the internet," said Herman, "it's a bit too flashy for my liking."

Sandi used the internet quite a lot, as did most of her friends, so she couldn't believe there was anybody who didn't.

But there was something about Herman she really liked.

He reminded her of the old fashioned characters from the books she'd read like Sherlock Holmes or Scott of the Antarctic.

"You're funny," she said.

"Is that good?" said Herman.

29

"Well, since the people of Sadsville certainly need cheering up, I think it is," said Sandi.

"Well, I'm glad I'm here in that case," said Herman, "and I think I may have solved the mystery as to why everyone is so sad."

"Wow, you solve mysteries too?" said Sandi in an impressed way. "Are you a secret agent or a detective?"

Herman thought about it for a moment.

"I've always thought of myself as more of an explorer or adventurer," he said, "...but maybe I am a detective too."

"Let's call you a Problem Solver," said Sandi.

"Herman Brimble. Problem Solver." Herman said out loud. It had a nice ring to it.

"Can I help you solve some problems?" asked Sandi.

"Of course," said Herman. "two heads are always better than one."

Sandi offered to 'High Five' Herman but he looked confused. They shook hands instead and they both smiled.

CHAPTER TEN

Herman and Sandi eventually arrived at an industrial estate on the outskirts of Sadsville.

On the side of one of the factory units was a huge plastic model of a packet of crisps.

'Brian's Gourmet Crisp Factory'

it said in big letters underneath

Herman and Sandi went into the factory reception area. Through a long line of windows they could see the main crisp production area.

There were conveyor belts, potato chopping machines and huge frying pans bubbling with hot oil.

But it was a large wooden crate in the 'Ingredients Preparation Area' that caught Herman's eye. Printed in large letters on the side it said:

GRADE A EXTREMELY STRONG ONIONS - FROM SCOTLAND

By the side a big machine was automatically peeling and slicing onions and depositing them on a conveyor belt.

The belt carried the raw, sliced onions across the factory to the crisp bagging area where another conveyor belt carrying lumps of cheese joined it.

Herman and Sandi watched as freshly cooked potato crisps were carefully loaded into individual packets and then bits of cheese and raw uncooked onions were added.

"ARE YOU THINKING WHAT I'M THINKING?" Herman said to Sandi.

Just then, a short, energetic man with wild ginger hair bounced from behind one of the machines.

"Helloooo," he said in a strong Scottish accent.

"The name's Brian, can I help yaa?"

"Brian?" said Sandi, "That's not a very Scottish sounding name... and if I'm not mistaken your accent is..."

"Scottish," Brian interrupted. "Aye lassie Scottish born and bred."

"My real name is Angus Connor Douglas Gordon Donald Wallace McLachlan but that wouldn't fit on the crisp packet, and I thought 'Brian's Crisps' sounded better, and anyway," Brian continued, "Brian means 'strength' and we like things strong in Scotland."

"So are the crisps made to your own recipe?" asked Herman.

"Passed down from my Grandma and her Grandma before that," said Brian proudly.

"Can we talk about your cheese and onion flavour in particular?" asked Sandi, realising what Herman had realised a few moments earlier.

"Made with the finest ingredients, aye," said Brian.

"And those would be?" continued Sandi.

"Potatoes," said Brian.

"Yes," said Herman "And?"

"Strong Scottish Cheddar cheese."

"Yes," said Sandi and Herman loudly at the same time. "And?"

"The strongest Scottish onions that I can lay my hands on!"

"And you use the cheese and onions as flavourings?" asked Herman.

"Flavourings?!" Brian almost exploded with indignation. "There's no artificial flavourings in Brian's Gourmet Crisps I'll have you know. We use the real thing."

"As in?" asked Sandi.

"As in whole bits of cheese and whole bits of onion," fizzed Brian.

"Cooked onion?" asked Herman, nervously.

Brian's face turned the same colour as his hair.

"COOKED?" he shouted.
"COOKED?!"

He bellowed in a voice so loud that it made all the pots and pans in the factory rattle.

"I'll have none of that namby-pamby cooked stuff flavouring Brian's Crisps," he screamed.

"But won't onions make..." Herman started.

"...people cry?" Sandi completed his sentence.

"Of course," said Brian, unperturbed.

"As my old Granny used to say,

"If they don't have you streaming... ...then there's no point in being"

Herman and Sandi looked at each other.

"Ahhahh," they both said at the same time.

CHAPTER ELEVEN

Over a cup of tea in the factory canteen Sandi and Herman explained to Brian what had been going on.

Everyone in Sadsville loved his crisps, especially the cheese and onion flavoured ones. But most cheese and onion crisps only contained cheese and onion *flavouring* not *actual* lumps of cheese and *actual* raw onions.

And the onions were making everybody's eyes water so everyone in Sadsville was always crying, making them look and feel very sad.

"Oh deary, deary me..." said Brian in a genuinely concerned way. "I wouldn't want that."

"Is there any chance we could try cooking the cheese and onions to make a special milder flavouring that we can use in some of the packets?" asked Herman.

"Aye for sure," agreed Brian. And soon he, Herman and Sandi were busy mixing ingredients in the factory kitchen.

Later that day, the first packet of

Brian's

New *Milder* *Gourmet Cheese and Onion*

Crisps

rolled off the production line.

CHAPTER TWELVE

Sandi and Herman walked back to the bus stop in the centre of Sadsville. Already the new crisps were proving very popular, and the streets were filled with happy, smiling faces.

"There'll be no more tears in Sadsville thanks to you Herman," said Sandi, giving him a hug.

"You ARE a problem solver. Perhaps it's because you're not from Sadsville?"

"Sometimes looking at things from the outside enables you to see things that you miss when you're looking at things from the inside," agreed Herman.

Then, in a slightly embarrassed way, he continued, "Would you like to help me solve other problems in the future?"

"I'd love to!" said Sandi.

"Just give me a call. I'll text you my number."

Herman looked at her blankly

"I don't have a mobile," he apologised. "Is there any way you could send me a letter or a postcard?"

"You're so funny," said Sandi. "Herman, my funny, eccentric new friend."

"Cool, as you say," said Herman. And they both laughed.

Just then a big double decker bus appeared at the top of the road and pulled to a halt at the bus stop.

"Where is this bus going?" Herman asked the bus driver.

"Not a million miles away," said the driver. And Herman was sure he saw him wink.

"Take good care of yourself," said Sandi as Herman climbed aboard.

"See you again soon."

"You most certainly will," replied Herman, and he knew he would.

They smiled and waved goodbye to each other.

CHAPTER THIRTEEN

It seemed like no time at all before the bus was pulling alongside the unfamiliar bus stop in the familiar street where Herman lived.

Herman hopped off the bus but when he turned around to thank the driver, the bus and the bus stop had disappeared.

"How odd," said Herman.

"I guess that really was a MAGICAL bus."

He opened the front door of Great Aunt Edna's house and headed straight for the room with all the books and timetables.

Still sitting on the table was a dusty old timetable of

BUSES TO THE VILLES.

Herman opened it and then noticed the strangest of things. On the page that had the timetable of buses to Sadsville it now just said:

Buses to Sadsville are no longer needed.

"That's very good to hear" said Herman.

"And not to worry," he continued "There are lots of other Villes for me to visit."

He focussed on one. Tiredsville.

"Sounds like a sleepy kind of place," he said.

"Maybe I'll have an adventure there tomorrow," he yawned "I like solving problems but right now I think it's cocoa and bed for me."

"The only problem is," he continued, "where is my favourite mug?"

THE END

Why is everyone in Tiredsville always so TIRED??

Will Herman be able to solve the mystery and turn Tiredsville into a place full of energy? Could it have something to do with Mr Harrington the mattress maker?

Pack your pyjamas and join Herman on the magical bus to Tiredsville to find out.

If you're sad for any reason, or you have a problem someone like me could help you solve, then call or email the lovely people at Childline who are there to support YOU, 24 HOURS A DAY 7 DAYS A WEEK. Before that, do check there are no slices of raw onion in your cheese and onion crisps!

WORRIED? We're here to Listen

**Call Childline on 0800 1111
or visit childline.org.uk/kids**
Whatever your worry, you can talk to us. It's free, you don't have to tell us your name, and you can chat about anything.

childline

ONLINE, ON THE PHONE, ANYTIME

Childline is a service provided by the NSPCC. ©NSPCC 2020. Registered charity England and Wales 216401. Scotland SC037717. Illustration by Emily Keenor. J20201088.

Lesson or Assembly Plan

Use in conjunction with Powerpoint and other resources available at
sadsville.co.uk

SADSVILLE KEY STAGE 2 LESSON OR ASSEMBLY PLAN

This lesson or assembly plan has been put together by the Martin Roberts Foundation to help you introduce the Sadsville Book to your children.

It is recommended that you give the children the opportunity to hear the story of Sadsville first. It's interesting to stop at regular intervals and ask why they think that everyone is sad. You can either:

1. Read the book aloud in a class or group
2. Watch the video of Basil Brush reading Sadsville that can be found on:

www.sadsville.co.uk

Before starting this lesson, please visit www.sadsville.co.uk and download the free resources to support you. These include:

- Sadsville Assembly / Lesson powerpoint
- Bag of Worries Worksheet
- Circle of Support Worksheet
- How to be a Good Listener Worksheet
- If I'm Feeling Sad Worksheet
- Tips for Wellbeing Poster
- Tips for Childhood Well-being for parents & carers

LESSON PLAN ABOUT FEELING SAD AND TALKING ABOUT EMOTIONS LINKING TO THE SADSVILLE BOOK

This Lesson or Assembly Plan can be used alongside the Powerpoint slides available as a free download from www.sadsville.co.uk

Age group:
Key Stage 2 (suggested 8/9 year olds but suitable for others)

Aims of this Lesson or Assembly Plan:

- To offers some simple guidance on how to deliver and explain the Sadsville book to your pupils
- To help children understand and express their emotions
- To encourage children to talk about their concerns - no problem is too big or too small
- To make children aware of how they can help themselves and one another and sources of other help, including Childline

Resources:

Lots of resources are available online at www.sadsville.co.uk including:

- Sadsville Assembly / Lesson slides
- Bag of Worries Worksheet
- Circle of Support Worksheet
- How to be a Good Listener Worksheet
- If I'm Feeling Sad Worksheet

- Tips for Wellbeing Poster
- Tips for Childhood Well-being for parents & carers
- A video recording of Basil Brush reading Sadsville
- A digital 'read along' version available on www.fonetti.com

OPTIONAL

- An onion, knife, chopping board and box of tissues for the demonstration in the Optional Introduction
- Drawstring bag and props to represent worries as per Slide 8 of the presentation.

TEACHER PRESENTATION	NOTES / ACTIONS
OPTIONAL BEGINNING Take the onion and begin peeling it and chopping it. "Today we are going to talk about feelings & emotions. In particular about feeling sad and crying".	Observe that it's not easy to prepare an onion without crying. A strong substance is released that causes the tear ducts in our eyes to water

INTRODUCTION

SLIDE 2: "LET'S TALK!"

Today we are going to talk about what makes us happy and what makes us sad. We will talk about our emotions, in particular feeling sad and the reasons why someone might cry.

I will also explain to you about Childline, a safe service just for children and young people where children can talk to someone if they have a problem that is making them feel unhappy or worried and they need to talk to a someone in confidence.

We have been reading / listening to the story 'SADSVILLE'. As you know this is a book about a place where people are always sad.

Today we are going to talk about feelings & emotions. In particular about feeling sad and crying.

An electronic read-along version of SADSVILLE is available free of charge by visiting www.fonetti.com and searching for 'Sadsville'.

SLIDE 3: "WHY MIGHT SOMEONE CRY?"

Why might someone cry?

Explain that there are a lot of reasons why people cry, and like laughter, tears simply reflect our innermost feelings.

Gather feedback from a few children.

TEACHER PRESENTATION	NOTES / ACTIONS
SLIDE 4 : "PEOPLE CRY FOR DIFFERENT REASONS" People can cry as a result of a wide range of emotions. For example: 1. Winning athletes on the podium are sometimes moved to tears as their national anthem is played. 2. Someone meeting up with a loved one they haven't seen for a while. 3. A parent watching a child sing or perform.	Ask children what sort of emotions might these people be feeling.
SLIDE 5 : "CRYING IS OK" People of all ages cry. Some people are moved to tears very easily. Explain that tears let out deep feelings and can help us to feel better.	Reassure children that it's alright to cry.

KEEPING FEELINGS INSIDE

SLIDE 6 : "WHY MIGHT SOMEONE KEEP THEIR WORRIES INSIDE" Why do you think someone might keep their worries hidden?	Ask for feedback from children i.e. feel silly, don't want to be embarrassed, don't want to hurt someone else's feelings.
SLIDE 7 : "WHAT DO YOU THINK ?" Do you think it's good to keep your worries inside? Explain that releasing emotions and showing how we feel often makes us feel better.	Gather feedback from a few children.
SLIDE 8 : "BAG OF WORRIES" What kind of things might make you feel sad, unhappy or worried? For each example given, place an item into the bag. Ask children to give suggestions on what makes them feel sad? The bag is starting to get really heavy. It would be difficult to carry all this sadness around if you didn't know who to turn to for help and support. Ask the children how this would make them feel?	Use an actual bag as physical prop. The empty bag is as light as a feather and easy to carry. But now get the children to load items into the bag. Imagine these items were worries that a child could be carrying around. Use the BAG OF WORRIES worksheet and help children draw or write what might be in their bag.

TEACHER PRESENTATION	NOTES
## SLIDE 9 : "BIG & SMALL FEELINGS" We have feelings that come and go every day. These are small feelings, such as feeling excited about something or nervous about something. Small feelings can feel very strong at times, but these feelings aren't usually a problem; they're all part of everyday life. We can usually keep these feelings inside as they pass quickly. "Can you think of small feelings that you've had today?"	Ask some children for examples: i.e. I'm not looking forward to my maths test later or I'm going to have tea with a friend today.
## SLIDE 10 & 11 : "BIG FEELINGS CAN BE BAD" We know that small feelings are all part of everyday life. But how about BIG feelings? Those ones that you feel EVERY DAY. Big feelings can change how we behave, how we see ourselves and the world around us and how we are with other people. Some of us might never experience these big feelings, but for those people that do, they can be really serious and shouldn't be ignored. "How do you think XX would behave if he was ALWAYS worried. Or if XX was ALWAYS scared?"	Refer back to previous answers on small feelings and ask how these children might feel if they felt like that ALL THE TIME.

'GOOD' SAD & 'BAD' SAD

## SLIDE 12 : "GOOD SAD & BAD SAD" Explain that not all types of sadness are the same. Sometimes its OK to be sad. It's just part of everyday life and growing up. Nobody likes to be sad but 'Good Sad' feelings, like small feelings will pass relatively quickly.	Ask children about little things that might make them sad.
## SLIDE 13 : "BAD SAD" Explain that there is a different kind of sadness that can be called 'Bad Sad'. These sad feelings can be caused by the actions of someone else. Like Big Feelings, this is a lot more serious and if you think you might be experiencing 'Bad Sad' you need to reach out for help and support.	Ask the children for examples of 'Bad Sad'. These could include being bullied, being left on your own for long periods (being neglected) or being physically or mentally abused.

WHY TALKING & LISTENING IS IMPORTANT

SLIDE 14 & 15 : "REACHING OUT FOR HELP / TRUSTED ADULT"

It can sometimes be difficult to understand how we are feeling and to tell the difference between our big and small feelings and 'Good Sad' and 'Bad Sad'.
"Who can help us understand the difference?"
Explain who a 'Trusted Adult' is:
- a teacher
- a parent or carer
- grandparents
- an aunt/uncle or any family member over 18 years old

Use the CIRCLE OF SUPPORT worksheet to help children record who they can talk to about how they are feeling.

SLIDE 16 : "SADSVILLE"

Remember the story of 'SADSVILLE' where everyone is always sad ALL THE TIME. The characters in Sadsville are so wrapped up in themselves and their worries that they don't talk to one another about what is making them sad - until a person from the outside comes in.

SLIDE 17 : "BEING A GOOD FRIEND"

It can sometimes be difficult to talk to someone if they seem too busy or you don't know what to say or how to start off the conversation.
"Can you think of words that you could say to make sure that person you are talking to listens carefully?"

And if someone wants to talk to you about how they feel, it is important to LISTEN. A friend could simply sit quietly beside someone who is upset. They may need to wait patiently if that person wants to be alone. A word of comfort or encouragement might help – or simply a reassuring touch. Someone who is upset is often helped if someone else will listen, not commenting or giving advice.

Draw out responses like "I've got something I want to talk about" or "I'm feeling really uncomfortable"

Ask children to offer ideas of how to be a good listener and friend. e.g. Sit side by side, make them feel comfortable to talk, listen carefully to what they say.

Use the HOW TO BE A GOOD LISTENER worksheet and ask children to complete by drawing or writing what they think makes someone a good listener.

SLIDE 18 : "IF YOU'RE FEELING SAD"

Remember if your feelings are getting too BIG to cope with on your own and you feel you want things to change...talking to someone else might really help.

Explain that children should tell a trusted adult if they feel hurt, unsafe, sad, worried or frightened and reassurance should be given that it is NEVER a child's fault to have these emotions. If the situation doesn't change it is very important for the child to keep speaking out and keep telling a trusted adult until the situation improves and changes.

Use the IF I'M FEELING SAD worksheet to guide children to think about what they can do to help themselves if they are feeling sad.

Hand out or post on wall TIPS for WELL BEING.

SLIDE 19 : "IF FEELINGS GET TOO BIG"

Explain that children contact Childline for all sorts of reasons so whatever the worry they will always listen carefully and trust whatever they are told. What a child says to Childline stays with Childline. It is a confidential 24 hour service, available every day of the year. Calls are free of charge. Children have a choice and do not have to give their name.

TIPS FOR WELL BEING YOU MAY WANT TO SHARE WITH CHILDREN

 Connect: Spend time with family and friends. Enjoy doing things together and talking to each other. Maybe help prepare some food or play a game. Take a break from gadgets.

 Be active: It keeps you physically healthy, and makes you feel good. Breathe in some fresh air.

 Keep learning: Try something new. Try a new hobby, or learn about something just because it interests you.

 Take a look at nature or the world around you.

 Give: Do something for a friend or relation/adult. As well as making them feel good, it can make you feel good too!

 Eat Well & Rest: Eat a balanced diet and make sure you're getting enough sleep.

We hope you found this Lesson Plan useful and that it created lots of discussion in your group or school. We'd love to hear back from you on how it went and what the children think of the Sadsville Book. You can complete a teacher questionnaire online at www.sadsville.co.uk . Here you will also find a feedback form to download and print out for your children to give their feedback on the book.

And just as a final reminder of what an important lesson this is, a few words from the NSPCC and Childline:

"Thank you for creating this highly entertaining and original way of raising children's awareness of how they can reach out for help through support services such as Childline. I wish the Sadsville book project every success."

Dame Esther Rantzen DBE, Founder & President of Childline

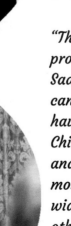

"The Sadsville book project will help support the work of the NSPCC to protect children today and prevent abuse from happening tomorrow... Sadsville introduces children to problem solving and explains that you can be sad for a number of different reasons and encourages them to have the confidence to seek help. The number and website for the Childline support services offers a call to action at the end of the book and provides children with a lifeline when needed the most. In the most extreme of cases, this lifeline saves lives. By distributing Sadsville widely, we put this message in to the hands of children who may not otherwise have known who to turn to for help, and although it is impossible to monitor how children come to hear about Childline, the number of additional children using the service as a direct result of this initiative could be highly significant."

Peter Wanless, CEO NSPCC

How can YOU help?

The Sadsville project is supported by charitable donations.

Perhaps your school, children, PTA or organisation could raise the money needed to provide a copy of Sadsville for every child in your school, or for children in places where it is most needed.

Visit sadsville.co.uk for fundraising ideas and more information

Could your class become Herman's Heroes?

We are looking to celebrate individual children and classes throughout the UK who are taking positive steps to improve the happiness of themselves and those around them.

Tell us about their initiatives, and we will feature them on the sadsville.co.uk website and in our social media.

The most heart-warming, effective and imaginative ideas will receive limited edition 'Herman's hero' badges and other prizes.

Visit sadsville.co.uk
for inspiration and more information!

Did You Enjoy 'Sadsville'?

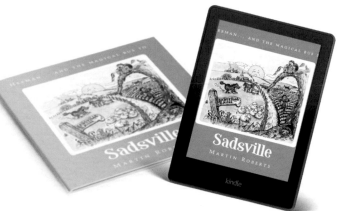

 Visit The Villes on YouTube to hear more stories being narrated...

Kindle and printed versions are available on

...or listen on your favourite Podcast platform:

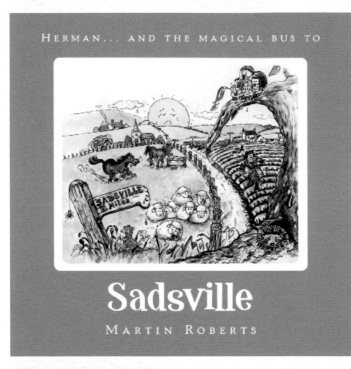
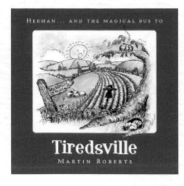

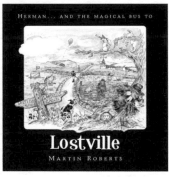
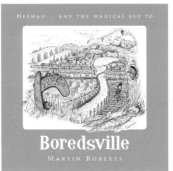

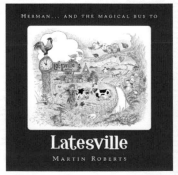

The Villes goes online!

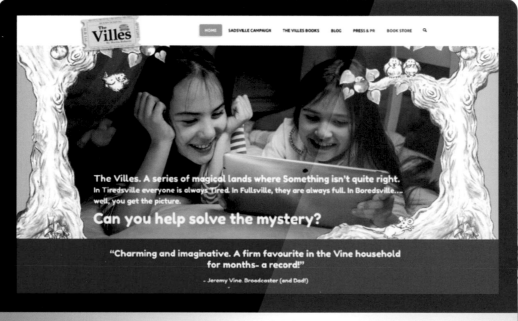

www.thevilles.com

Keep track of my journey as I travel the Country in search of more heroes and friends! Come and join in the fun!

Sadsville and Fonetti

I'm delighted that Sadsville is available on Fonetti.

Not only does it allow Sadsville to reach readers globally and promote wellbeing across the world, it helps children read independently.

With Fonetti, children don't need a grown-up to help them read. They have the opportunity to read to themselves with the support of speech recognition technology that gives them tips to pronounce any tricky words they struggle with.

Fonetti helps children understand how powerful their voice can be - not just when reading but in helping others too, taking them on a journey from Sadsville to Happyville.

Find out more at:
fonetti.com

Have you met Fonetti?

Fonetti makes reading fun.

It's the world's first listening bookshop, where shelves of stories are waiting with the swipe of a screen. Fonetti listens and rewards as children read.

When they get the words right, they turn green, if they get stuck, they simply double tap for a clue.

It perfects their pronunciation, boosts their literacy and builds their confidence with every page they turn.

Approved by the Department for Education's Hungry Little Minds Campaign as a platform to practise reading on; Fonetti is changing the way children read globally.

Fonetti has a range of resources and a portal specifically to support schools, and also houses all of 'The Villes' books.

Find us at:

fonetti.com

(Android Nov 2020)

Department for Education

ORGANISATIONS THAT CAN HELP

kidscape.org.uk
parentsupport@kidscape.org.uk

Provides children, families, carers and professionals with advice, training and practical tools to prevent and deal with bullying.

bulliesout.com

mentorsonline@bulliesout.com

Bullies Out work through schools and community settings to educate, train, support and raise awareness of bullying.

familylives.org.uk

0808 800 2222

Family Lives provides targeted early intervention and crisis support to families who are struggling. The issues they support families with include family breakdown, challenging relationships and behaviour, debt, and emotional and mental wellbeing.

beateatingdisorders.org.uk

Helpline 0808 801 0677

Youthline 0808 801 0711

1:1 web chat available

via website.

A champion, guide and friend to anyone affected by eating disorders, giving individuals experiencing an eating disorder and their loved ones a place where they feel listened to, supported and empowered.

www.griefencounter.org.uk

0808 802 0111

Provides support and services to bereaved children, young people and their families.

themix.org.uk

0808 808 4994

The Mix help young people take on any challenge they're facing - from mental health to money, from homelessness to finding a job, from break-ups to drugs. Reach them via the online community, on social, through their free, confidential helpline or their counselling service.

ORGANISATIONS THAT CAN HELP

childline.org.uk

0800 1111

Childline is there to help anyone under 19 in the UK with any issue . Children can talk about anything with them. Whether it's something big or small, their trained counsellors are there to support them 24-7.

mind.org.uk

0300 123 3393

Text service available on 86463

Mind provides advice and support to empower anyone experiencing a mental health problem. The Infoline offers callers confidential help for the price of a local call. They have a network of local associations in England and Wales to which people can turn for help.

youngminds.org.uk

0808 802 5544

Crisis Text service: Text: YM to 85258.

UK charity committed to improving the emotional wellbeing and mental health of children and young people.

place2be.org.uk

Place2Be is a children's mental health charity with over 25 years' experience working with pupils, families and staff in UK schools. They provide mental health support in schools through one-to-one and group counselling using tried and tested methods backed by research.

supportline.org.uk

01708 765200

Offers a confidential emotional support to children, young adults and adults by telephone, email and post. Aimed at those who are socially isolated, vulnerable, at risk groups and victims of any form of abuse.

samaritans.org

116123

Provide a confidential service for people in despair and who feel suicidal. Whatever you're going through, a Samaritan will face it with you. They are available 24 hours a day, 365 days a year.

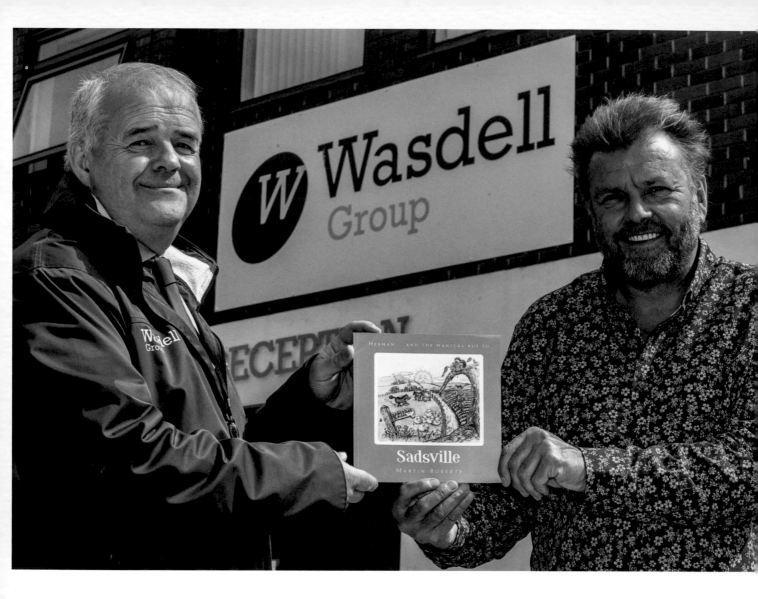

The Wasdell Group is pleased to help the Martin Roberts Foundation place a copy of this book in every primary school in the United Kingdom.

With sincere thanks to the following for their invaluable support:

Printed and bound in Great Britain by
Gemini Print
Unit A1, Dolphin Way, Shoreham-by-Sea, West Sussex, BN43 6NZ
www.gemini-print.co.uk

Design and Layout by
Postscript,
15 Stony Street, Frome, Somerset, BA11 1BU
www.postscriptfrome.co.uk

MARTIN ROBERTS FOUNDATION
CHILD WELLBEING & EDUCATION

The Martin Roberts Foundation has been created to raise funds to help children and young people develop skills and capabilities that will assist them in their journey to adulthood, through a range of educational initiatives and support activities.

The Foundation is currently embarking on a major fundraising campaign to enable the distribution of *Sadsville*, part of *The Villes* series, to all 8 & 9 year olds in the UK. *Sadsville* supports the in-school safeguarding curriculum, and raises awareness of the issues surrounding being sad for whatever reason, and guides children to where they can get help. If enough funds can be raised, it will be distributed for free through schools, health centres, and other agencies across England & Wales.

CHARITY NO: 1172905   For more information or to offer support, please visit www.martinrobertsfoundation.org.uk

HERMAN'S TIPS
IF YOU'RE FEELING SAD

Are you feeling 'Good' sad or 'Bad' sad?

Sometimes it's OK to feel sad - like when your holiday ends, your friend moves away or your pet dies. These things are all part of life and the feelings will pass. That's 'Good' sad.

'Bad' sad is when someone is being mean or asking you to do something you don't want to do. Perhaps something is causing you to be worried or frightened, or you feel sad for no real reason. Usually 'Bad' sad goes on for much longer.

Help Yourself
Do what I do and take a step back from the situation you're in to try to work out what's making you sad. What would make things better? Try to do something that makes you happy.

Talk to a Trusted Friend
Sharing your feelings with a friend can make you feel better.

Talk to a Trusted Adult
Like a teacher, coach, parent or relative. They may be able to help you understand if you're feeling 'Good' sad or 'Bad' sad and help you in either case.

Ask for Help
There are organisations like Childline with people who want to help you, so don't be afraid to get in touch.

childline

ONLINE, ON THE PHONE, ANYTIME
childline.org.uk | 0800 1111

Whatever your worry, call us and a friendly person will be there to listen. **It's free, you don't have to tell us your name, and we're here all day and night.**